Autism
How to help your young child

AUTHORS

**Leicestershire County Council,
Education Department**

Autism Outreach Team
Penny Barratt

Educational Psychology Service
Christine Cassell
Bessie Hayes
Tink Reader
Philip Whitaker

Fosse Health Trust, National Health Service

Speech and Language Therapy Service
Alison Parkinson

The National Autistic Society

First published 1998
by The National Autistic Society
393 City Road
London EC1V 1NE

ISBN 1 899280 65 0

Designed by Cottier & Sidaway Design Partnership

Printed in Great Britain by F Crowe & Sons Limited

Acknowledgements

This booklet was produced by the authors during the course of their work for Fosse Health Trust and Leicestershire County Council. It arose because many parents of young children with autism ask for guidance about how to help their child, and from a realisation that there is little published along these lines.

We should like to thank the many parents and colleagues who have taken time to comment on draft versions and those members of the support staff who have helped with the preparation of the booklet.

Contents

UNIT 3: Imagination and the need for sameness

General introduction

Children with autism have difficulties in three main areas:

- social interaction
- all aspects of communication (verbal and non-verbal)
- rigidity of thinking and lack of imagination.

Most children with autism also show some unusual repetitive mannerisms. When a child with autism is identified, it is the overall pattern of behaviour and difficulties which is considered, rather than any one feature on its own.

Autism affects children in all walks of life, from all countries and cultures, and at all levels of ability. However, children with autism vary enormously. The effects of autism can be mild or severe. For any child the picture will be affected by age and sex, personality and any other disability the child may have.

Helping a child with autism can be very demanding and progress may be slow and limited. We hope you and your family find some of the following suggestions helpful. Some may be more relevant to your child than others and some may not apply at all. Try to find your child among the 'pen-pictures'. Look to see if there are any suggestions you can use. If something doesn't work for you, don't worry. Tackle something else, or make up some ideas for yourself along similar lines. There is a lot of overlap between the sections, and as you read through you will see that the same ideas come up again and again, in slightly different ways.

At the back of this booklet there are some telephone numbers and addresses of services and organisations which you may find helpful.

Index of pen-pictures

UNIT 1: SOCIAL INTERACTION

4

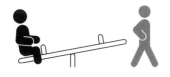
UNIT 2: COMMUNICATION

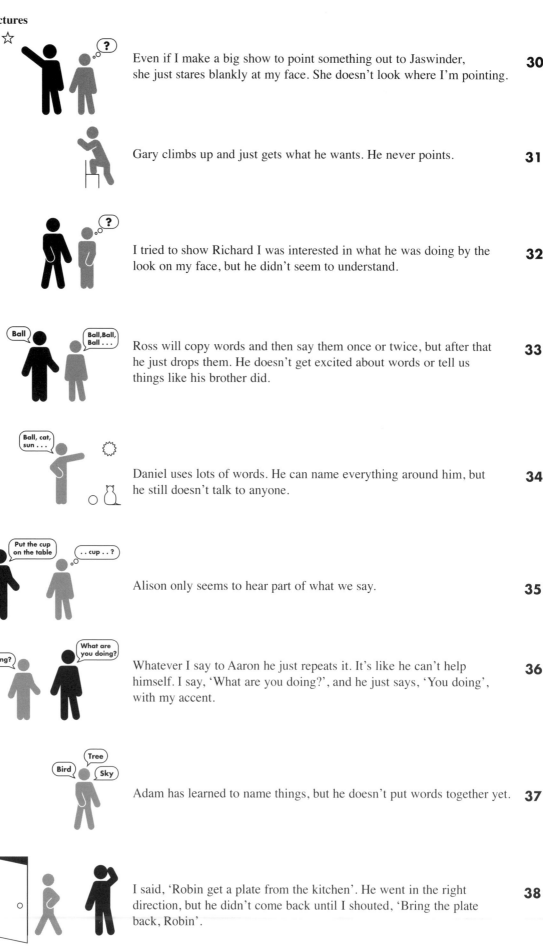

6

UNIT 3: IMAGINATION AND THE NEED FOR SAMENESS

Index of pen-pictures

UNIT 1: Social interaction

When they are born, most babies seem ready to become sociable and to develop communication skills. They have a natural preference for faces. From the early days of life they are particularly interested in any moving human face which comes near. Young children just seem to **know** that people are important: to turn to for comfort, to share moments of pleasure with, to look to for guidance and to learn from. They quickly learn to get help from adults when they want something.

Studies of mothers and young babies show "conversations" between them. There is a pattern of turn-taking and shared understanding, long before language with words develops. Babies quickly tune in to their parents. They pick up those unspoken messages which are communicated by facial expression and body language. In this way they learn what is expected of them and when it is all right to behave in a particular way. They are able to recognise when someone is happy or upset and what that means. Gradually they learn the unspoken rules about how to behave with people.

Children with autism find all this very difficult. They may seem less interested in people. They find it hard to see things from another person's point of view, and they often seem trapped in a world of their own.

In this unit we shall be looking under separate section headings at:

- social awareness and interest
- shared attention
- social play.

Some general points

- Remember that you are trying to improve the quality of life for your child and all those around him. You are trying to help him to behave in a more socially acceptable way so that others respond to him better and so that he is happier.

- Get to know your child thoroughly. What does he like and dislike? What does he want or need? What does he respond to? Who gets the most from him? What can he do? What is he good at? Make some notes for yourself as you notice things or as things occur to you. You might like to keep a diary.

- **Don't** try to devote every waking minute to him. Do **try** to make better use of time you spend with him anyway.

- Protect him from teasing by his brothers and sisters, or from being bullied by other children. Help them to understand and to allow for his odd ways.

- Make his day predictable and safe. Establish regular and meaningful routines, with few words to begin with, so that he can understand his day and anticipate what is going to happen next. Avoid sudden changes or requests, but when they are necessary, prepare him and help him to face them.

■ Remember that many of the suggested activities would usually be undertaken with a much younger child. You may feel foolish. It may be physically difficult to play baby games with a child long past the toddler stage, but it may be one of the most helpful things that you can do. On the other hand make sure that you keep the age and sex of your child, and the situation, in mind. Encourage other people to be gentle with him, patient and firm, but also considerate.

■ Encourage family members to help by doing things in the same way. Consistency is important as it will help your child to understand what is happening and to know what is expected of him.

■ Don't forget to talk to your child whenever you are doing things together.

Social awareness and interest

Before you start

■ With babies and small children use the contact which occurs naturally during daily routines like nappy changing, dressing, bath times and meal times. Make these 'fun' times, trying to allow time for unhurried playing with fingers, toes, hair and faces.

■ Try to break in on his world. Now and again **impose** your presence on him. Try to interact with him a little at a time. Little and often throughout the day is better than having long intense sessions.

■ Keep calm and avoid raised, excited voices. Don't persist in trying to make contact with him when you are feeling upset or irritated. Use gentle, slow movements, with frequent smiles and touches. Try to be warm but matter of fact, rather than over enthusiastic.

■ When playing with him or carrying out activities such as washing or dressing, get down to his level by sitting or kneeling on the floor. When you are trying to work with him in a more structured way, use a small table with a chair at the right height.

Touching: getting close

"Adam seems to live in a world of his own. He doesn't take any notice of other people, especially children."

What to look out for

■ Some children with autism may seem aloof, or very isolated and lonely.

■ They may avoid other children, either ignoring them or walking over them as if they are not there.

■ Others hit or push children, for no obvious reason.

■ Sometimes it may seem that they treat everyone the same way, not even making a difference for their mother or father.

Things to try

■ Use more touching than would be usual for his age, even if to start with he shows no signs of enjoying it.

■ Use a range of movements while lifting or carrying him around the house – swaying, dancing, swinging, lowering and lifting, pausing and starting again. Stop if he objects, or if you see signs of distress. Then try it again later on.

■ Introduce games which involve holding and cuddling, and try to get some pleasure from them yourself.

■ Because Adam does not take any notice of **you**, make sure you don't ignore him. When approaching him, or sitting alongside him, treat him as if he **is** aware that you are there, and may react to your presence at any time.

■ To begin with, approach and stay near for a few seconds only. Perhaps give a toy or say 'hello', before going away. When he seems comfortable with this, stay a little longer each time until he accepts your continuous presence.

■ Introduce your presence: use a familiar touch, say his name and talk to him without demanding a reaction. For example, make a comment about what he is doing.

■ Bring yourself to his attention when you enter or leave the room. Go up to him, say his name, touch him or give him a hug. On leaving, wave and say 'good-bye'. Make this a regular pattern even if to begin with you get little response or interest.

Touching: getting even closer

"Sophie doesn't like being touched or held."

What to look out for

■ An early sign of autism can be when a baby is difficult to hold, because she doesn't 'cuddle-in' or adjust her body to yours. You may not have noticed it much at the time, but may realise when you look back.

■ Some children with autism get agitated if people are near, and may get up and move away.

■ Some don't like being touched lightly or in a hesitant way.

■ Some accept a cuddle, but only after they have backed on to your lap. See **Helping him to come to you – p14**.

Things to try

■ Touch and handle her in a loving way. Cuddle and stroke her; smooth cream or talc on at bath time. Roll her in a warm blanket or soft towel and give her a hug. Touch her with your finger tips or the flat of your hand, your cheek or your hair. Nuzzle her or blow 'raspberries' on different parts of her body.

■ When you go to touch her, be confident in your movements. She may respond better to firm handling rather than light touches.

■ Occupy yourself alongside her when she is playing. Now and then touch or take one of her toys and give her something of yours instead.

■ Reach out now and then to take Sophie's hand and pull her towards you for a brief cuddle. When she accepts this don't pull as hard, but leave her to finish the move towards you.

Touching: moving on from small beginnings

"Michael varies a lot in how much he will let you touch him, and it is quite unpredictable."

What to look out for

■ Some children with autism are lively and active. Some show affection and like a cuddle.

■ Some like 'rough and tumble' play, but reject more casual and gentle touches.

■ Some can be very demanding and 'clingy', especially with their mother.

■ Some have 'favourite' people who can get more from them.

Things to try

■ Encourage Michael's involvement with you. Find ways to let him know how pleased you are. Look out for any sign of interest in other people and try to get **them** to react with pleasure as well.

■ Touch him lightly on the cheek, arm or hand **before** you pick him up or start a rough and tumble game.

■ Use rough and tumble or chasing games, but don't overdo it, or let it get to the point where he becomes over-excited.

■ Find time and opportunity for him to make contact with people naturally. Gradually help him to build on this, for example by using different greetings, or by encouraging him to greet different people.

■ Teach him how to wave 'bye bye' or hold up his arms when he wants to be lifted or swung. To begin with stand behind him and actually hold his hands or arms. Get him to make the gestures you want to another person, or get **someone else** to help him make the gestures to you. Do this regularly in the same daily situations. Try to reduce **your** involvement as **he** shows signs of doing the right thing in the right place and at the right time. See **Unit 2 – Understanding gestures – p30.**

■ When he is able to do so, get him to take messages, carry out simple errands or follow instructions like, 'Take this to Daddy'.

Hurt and comfort: making things safe

"We never know if Reena is happy or sad. In fact she rarely shows pleasure or pain. Even when she hurts herself badly she doesn't come for comfort or let us try to comfort her."

What to look out for

■ Some children with autism do not seem to react to pain. They may not cry when they are hurt, and may show little interest in seeking comfort.

■ Often they show little or no awareness of danger.

■ Watch out for Reena hurting herself. Perhaps she gives unusual signals such as a particular sound or word.

■ Identify the danger points in each room (eg the fireplace, electric sockets, sharp corners, radiators).

Things to try

■ It may be possible to teach Reena how to avoid danger. If she is about to touch something dangerous, physically stop her with a sharp 'No' and perhaps with an intake of breath.

■ When she is a little older, or when you think she is understanding, try drawing barrier lines in chalk or tape on the floor, around a heater for example. Teach her not to step over the line and praise or cuddle her for not doing so.

■ If you think she has been hurt, behave **as if** she has felt pain and offer cuddles, reassurance and comfort, even if she seems indifferent. Find other ways to comfort her, for example by bringing a favourite blanket or toy and cuddling it together, or by sitting alongside and stroking her arm while talking or singing in a soothing tone.

Learning not to feel embarrassed

"Nikesh is awful when people come round. He goes and touches them. It's all wrong."

What to look out for

■ Some children with autism seem to avoid people most of the time but then suddenly come up close. They may touch your face, play with your hair or poke at your eyes.

■ It can be embarrassing if your child strokes a visitor's leg, smells at them or even licks them.

■ Sometimes jewellery or clothing seem to attract the child more than the person wearing them.

■ This kind of behaviour will probably feel impersonal because the child seems to be treating people as if they are objects, but it **is** an important start that you can build on.

Things to try

■ To begin with try to accept and welcome Nikesh's approaches, however unusual they may be. Any sort of approach is better than none and should be encouraged. Teach him alternative ways of touching by taking his hand and helping him to stroke an arm or a cheek instead, very gently. Show him how to touch the family pet or a younger brother or sister in a similar way, with hugs and approval all round.

■ Instead of feeling embarrassed or annoyed, try to **show** and **tell** Nikesh what to do: how to do it, when to do it and when not to do it. Give him plenty of time to respond. Hopefully he will learn how to make more acceptable approaches.

■ If he behaves in an embarrassing way when you've got company, try to distract him. Give him something to do you know he likes.

■ Explain to visitors that Nikesh doesn't mean to be rude. He's got difficulties which are not his fault. It may help to explain, perhaps beforehand, that he is autistic.

■ When Nikesh comes **too** close, ease yourself away naturally but without rejecting him or showing annoyance.

■ Eventually you should be able to prompt him to do the right thing. For example say, 'Go and take Grandpa's hand, Nikesh'; and don't forget to praise him.

Helping him to come to you

*"When Christopher comes up it's always **behind** me, or he'll back onto my knee like I'm a chair."*

What to look out for

■ Children with autism often make what seem to be awkward approaches which are not 'face to face'.

■ Some enjoy rubbing against their parent's back, maybe with their T–shirt pulled up so that their skin makes direct contact with clothing.

■ They may come and put their arms around your knees from behind when you are standing.

■ Some back towards people in an impersonal way almost as if they are furniture.

Things to try

■ As Christopher moves behind you, try to anticipate the moment he will reach you; turn your head briefly as he grasps your knees, smile and say, 'Hello'. When you have managed this a time or two, gradually turn your body to greet him and bend down, extending the time of face to face contact with each approach.

■ As Christopher backs onto your knee turn him briefly, within the circle of your arms or between your knees, before turning him away from you again. As before, gradually increase the time he is facing you.

Looking: face to face

"I just can't get Nadeem to look at me even if I get really cross. I never know what he wants or how he's feeling."

What to look out for

- A child with autism may look aside or past people, rather than directly at them.

- He may seem as if he's not listening, but you sense that he is **really** even though he doesn't turn to his name.

- Your mood may seem to make no difference to him.

- Many children with autism don't use facial expression, or make gestures to let you know what they want.

Things to try

- Establish contact with Nadeem in any way you can. Make good use of vision, hearing and touch.

- When you want him to look at you, move into his line of sight and say 'Nadeem, look.'

- You may find it helps to touch his cheek and gently turn his head towards you, if he will allow it, as you say his name.

- Encourage him to touch or point to features, fingers and toes, etc (both his and yours) as you name them. Play games and sing songs which emphasise body parts.

- Guide his hands to feel your face or throat while you make noises, exaggerated movements or funny faces.

- Play games to encourage looking, listening and touching. Bath time is a particularly good time for this. Guide his hands and make funny noises or expressions as he touches you, such as a 'peep peep' sound as he touches your nose, or a rapid opening and closing of your mouth when he touches your lips. Once he realises that he can make **you** do something, he may want to try it again for himself.

- Show him and tell him who he is, saying 'Nadeem's nose, Nadeem's eyes' as you touch him.

- Encourage Nadeem to take notice of you and, eventually, to learn to look at your face. Get down to his level, by kneeling or sitting on the floor. Sit facing him, rather than alongside, in the right line of sight should he choose to glance at you. Don't **expect** eye contact but react with pleasure and approval if it comes, however fleetingly. Hold the thing he is interested in, or which he wants, beside your face and close to your eyes. Say something like, 'Nadeem, look'.

Looking: better eye contact

"We can't get Sam to look at us properly."

What to look out for

- Some children with autism show an absence of eye contact, but it is more common to find **unusual** eye contact.

- They may look at people with a rapid sweeping or sideways glance and it is difficult to keep them looking at you.

- They may look at your clothes, your hair or your jewellery rather than at your eyes or your face.

- Sometimes they may lower their eyelids, cover their eyes with their hands or look away when you try to catch their eye.

- Some may stare at people unblinking, especially strangers or visitors.

- At times they may come up to examine people, getting very close and making them uncomfortable.

Things to try

- When you notice that Sam's interest has been caught by your dangly earrings or something you are wearing round your neck, try to use this interest to draw his attention to you as a person. Move your head slightly to make eye contact if you can.

- Try putting a novel hat or something funny on your head. Pull it over your eyes then peep out at him with a smile.

- Blow soap bubbles gently, encouraging him to watch them as they float away and pop. Try to start the bubbles low down between you so that they float up past your face. You can try to catch his gaze as they pass.

- If you see that Sam is looking at something, talk to him about it and move into the line of his gaze as you talk. If you find Sam looking at you, respond with a smile and a greeting, or make conversation. Turn away naturally, but try to catch his gaze again and repeat.

- When Sam comes too close try not to jerk away. Say 'Hello', and smile while you slowly move your head back or move him gently a little further away.

- Try to encourage eye contact while you are playing with him. Stop suddenly and wait in the hope that Sam will look at you. If he does, treat it as a signal to carry on. If possible develop this into turn–taking play. See **Social play – p21.**

- If Sam stares, try not to be embarrassed but avoid staring back. Hold his gaze for a while and then look away, glancing back later in a natural way.

- Play chasing games or stop/go running games with, 'Ready, steady' then a hand signal with, 'Go'. Encourage Sam to watch and you may find that he looks to see if you are watching him, before he runs away.

- Tap him firmly on the hand, arm or shoulder to get his attention. Bring something from behind your back to show him, or open your hand to show him what you have hidden in it.

- If he is beginning to understand joking and humour, try sorting things into two different boxes, perhaps one for bricks and one for other toys. Pretend to put something in the wrong box and say, 'No', with a shake of the head. Encourage him to do the same, waiting for you to say, 'Yes', or, 'No'. Wait for him to give a 'check back' look before putting the object in the correct box.

Understanding other people: looking for clues

"David doesn't pick up the clues about how I am feeling."

What to look out for

- Some children with autism can't interpret gestures and expressions and may, for example, behave as if they think you are angry, when you are really in a good mood.

- A common problem is that they feel children are being rough and threatening, when they are just running around.

- Often children with autism can't use signs and gestures properly themselves and they may make odd gestures or grimaces, which don't mean anything, or may laugh or shout for no good reason.

Things to try

- Talk to David about what people are doing and what is going to happen next. Prepare him for unfamiliar situations when people may dress or behave in ways he has not met before.

- You may need to explain what you feel or mean when you use gestures, such as a shrug for 'don't know' or pursed lips for disapproval. Tell David what it means, or what you feel like, when you laugh or cry or get angry.

- Look at books or pictures together. Say, 'Let's find a happy face,' or 'Which one is cross?'

- Cut out pictures of faces from magazines. Make a 'happy' collection, sticking them on paper to go up on the kitchen wall. See **Unit 2 – Understanding gestures – p30**.

Learning to listen

"Charles never seems to listen to anything. He doesn't turn to his name and he just doesn't seem to hear when you talk to him."

*"Victor seems deaf to loud sounds, but he always hears the rustle of a sweet paper. Sometimes, he is **really** startled by a quiet sound."*

What to look out for

- Some children with autism become very frightened or upset on hearing certain harmless sounds.

- Some may react differently at different times and may, for example, sometimes respond to your voice or their name being called, but not at other times.

- Most like the sound of music, especially when it has a strong rhythm.

- Occasionally a child with autism will get confused about sights and sounds. He may cover his eyes to shut out a sound, or cover his ears when he doesn't want to see something.

Things to try

- Use signals to gain his attention – for example touch his ear for 'listen' and his cheek for 'look'.

- When you start to talk to him, use his name and wait until you think you have the best attention he is capable of. If you can, use the same phrase like, 'Charles, listen'.

- When working or playing with him, try to reduce any background noise or distractions.

- Talk or sing quietly alongside him, while carrying out your daily chores. Use familiar songs and everyday sayings, some connected with times of the day (mealtimes, bath time, bed time) and some repeated regularly throughout the day.

- Introduce him to a wide range of sounds of different loudness and pitch.

- Make music or simple rhythms with instruments or using household objects such as spoons, pan lids or a cardboard box and stick. Encourage him to take part. Leave gaps for him to fill and act **as if** you expect him to take part. If he doesn't, then continue, but keep on leaving gaps, aiming eventually to get him to take turns, where you do something and then he does something. Encourage brothers and sisters to play with him in the same way.

- Use music and movement to help you to interact with him. Sing with him. Make up songs about what you are both doing using familiar tunes like 'This is the way we ...'. Encourage him to march, hop or jump in time to the music. Pick him up and dance or sway him around.

- Use simple action rhymes and songs, trying to build up suspense for the punch line. Leave a pause that is slightly longer than feels comfortable, in the hope that he may help out with the actions or sounds.

- Encourage him to sit still, and look and listen for short periods (very short to begin with, but gradually extending). He might like a special cushion to sit on while you are listening to a tape or story together.

- Reassure him, comfort him and do what you can, to stop a sound if it is causing distress. If necessary move him away. If it is a sound you can't control like that of the vacuum cleaner, warn him when it is about to start. To begin with let him stay in the next room with someone else. Then, when you think he is ready, try to help him to tolerate more and more, bringing him nearer. Only gradually expect him to manage it on his own. Sometimes you can use a softer, quieter version of a hated sound to help build up his tolerance. You might be able to use a tape recorder for this.

■ As you control the sound level for him, use a phrase like, 'Too noisy' or, 'Turn it down'. If he is able to use words himself, encourage him if he starts to copy what you say. It may take a long time, but one day he may say it for himself.

Shared attention

Before you start

■ Always keep in mind that it is **shared** interest and attention you are working for, not just your child's interest in the **things** you are both playing with.

■ Many children with autism will not realise that **you** might be interested in what **they** are doing. They may not show you things or try to make you watch them.

■ Many will touch and name pictures or objects in a mechanical way, which does not depend on anyone else being there to listen or see. Your child will need to learn that we point in order to involve other people.

Look at this!

"James has never once brought anything to show me."

What to look out for

■ Unlike most children, children with autism don't usually attract people's attention to the things they are interested in, by pointing or sharing glances. They don't seem to realise that **you** might be interested in **them**.

■ They don't understand how to **share** interest and do not look where **you** are looking, even if you point and say, 'Look!'

■ Their interest is confined to things which are obvious and close by, and they don't realise that other people may also be interested.

Things to try

■ Continue to show him things which you find interesting even though you seem to be getting little response. Pay attention to **him** and comment on what **he** is doing.

■ Link your praise and attention, and signs of affection, directly to what he is doing at that moment.

■ Make your presence more obvious and interesting. Choose to do things yourself which you think he might find interesting. Bring what you are doing close to him and attract his attention.

■ Show him things, especially if you can touch them, when you are out on a walk. Try to keep it simple, showing one thing at a time. Keep any talking simple and clear; talk about what you are looking at. Help him to understand what you mean with gestures and actions.

- If James is standing in front of you with a toy, react **as if** it is being shown or offered to you. Look at it or hold it. Show interest and talk about it before returning it. Be alert to the possibility that James **may** be trying to convey a message to you with the toy.

- If you see that James is interested in something, follow his gaze and show interest yourself. Try to make him feel that you are sharing something.

- Use books. Those with things hiding under flaps are particularly useful. Really show James **your** enjoyment of the book. Talk about what you see and ask, 'Where's Spot hiding?' etc.

- Gradually prompt him into a wider range of showing. Say, 'Mummy wants to see....' or, 'Let's look at that'. Once he is able to look at something with you, draw his attention to details, or working parts, or talk about what is happening in a picture.

- Try to get James to point or gesture. Look at things together and say, 'Where's the...?'. You may find to begin with that holding his hand lightly, or allowing him to hold yours, is a help. Gradually reduce the amount of guidance you give and encourage him to take over. See **Unit 2 – Communication – p25.**

- When he is ready, get him to show someone else what you've both been doing.

- If he has finished a puzzle, or done a drawing, encourage him to show this around.

Doing things together

*"Tom shows **some** interest in toys and play, and he will tolerate people being near as long as they don't interfere or join in."*

What to look out for

- Some children with autism may show things briefly, or point at them while naming them, but not as a way of gaining your interest and attention.

- Some will point at things they want, and may take your hand to make it do things for them, but they won't do the things for themselves, using their own hands.

- Many able children with autism can play well, as long as it is something **they** have started, but they do not follow **your** lead or take up any of your suggestions.

Things to try

- Teach Tom how to give things. Hold his wrist lightly and guide his hand towards you. Take the object, react to it with pleasure as if it had been given, then return it. Give him things **you** find interesting, then ask for and guide their return.

- Play 'one for Mummy and one for Tom' type games, dividing things between you. Later extend this to involve other children.

- Introduce the idea of 'Which one does Tom like?' and talk about; 'Tom's favourite, Mummy's favourite, Daddy's favourite'.

- React to, or even interrupt, his play from across the room. Comment, exclaim or laugh and ask, 'Let Mummy see?' or say 'Do another jump'.

- Play games like 'Ready-steady-go' while he jumps from a step or does a run across the room. Say the words slowly, building up the anticipation and try to get him to wait for the, 'go'.

- When you notice Tom doing anything, or making sounds, copy him and act **as if** the sounds or actions mean something. Make a game of imitating him, but concentrate on sharing **his** interest and take care not to make fun of him. Pause, wait for a reaction and start again. Leave gaps for him even though he may not fill them to begin with. Eventually, once you have established patterns of imitation started by him, you can introduce a few sounds or actions of your own, aiming to get **him** imitating **you**. See **Unit 2 – Making sounds – p27**.

- Encourage Tom to show you things he wants. Allow him to take you to what he wants or to take hold of your hand to get things for him. Sometimes pretend not to understand. Shape his hand into a point and gently guide it to the right place. Use real objects to begin with, while encouraging him to reach or point. Later on you can try using pictures or photographs of everyday things you know he might want. Lay out several at a time. Encourage him to choose and show you what he means. Then you might take it a step further by expecting him to bring you the right picture (which he has selected himself) **before** you give him what he wants.

- Once Tom is tolerating your playing alongside him, gradually introduce something new. For example if you are both adding to a long line of blocks, you could introduce one which turns a corner, or one which stands on top of the others. He is unlikely to accept it the first time, but keep on and eventually he will. Make the most of the look he might give you when you have altered his pattern. Change things back and look at him with a smile, showing him that his look has **meant** something to you. Make other changes to his routines, but don't try to tease him, unless he is enjoying the joke.

Social play

Before you start

- We have talked about improving your child's awareness of people, helping him to understand social routines, and encouraging him to share interest and attention. Next we shall focus on building interaction and 'give and take', so that he can **experience** the pleasure which comes from playing with people, as opposed to playing with things.

- Try to develop a working and playing relationship with your child. Establish places, chairs and tables, and regular times, when he knows that you will give him attention.

Play with me

"Sarah has never shown any interest in baby games like 'peek-a-boo'."

"Hannah never tries to get me to play with her and when I try to play with her she pushes my hands away or just walks off. She isn't bothered."

What to look out for

■ Many children with autism don't respond when their parents try to play with them.

■ They may seem passive, and just sit. Alternatively they may turn away, walk away or become agitated.

■ They may appear uninterested even if you are very obviously busy around them with household chores.

■ Many don't seem to want any response from their parents or anyone else.

Things to try

■ Start with quiet play activities. Set things up, and get Sarah settled and interested in something. Then sit alongside, just watching to begin with. When she tolerates this, you can extend it to playing alongside and then to intervening a little. Persist in trying to reduce her isolation. If she gets angry or distressed you may need to leave it for a while, but you could try again later.

■ Allow time for animated baby games such as 'peek-a-boo', 'round and round the garden', 'Mummy's coming' etc. Carry on even if you think she is not responding – she will eventually. Use lots of physical contact games such as bouncing her on your knees and dropping her between them to, 'This is the way the lady rides' or, 'Ride a cock horse'.

■ Use lap games. If necessary start with her sitting with her back to you. Find out which songs or games she seems to like. Then use those games with her facing you, but not too close (perhaps at the edge of your knees) for short periods. Don't expect eye contact or obvious co-operation to start with. Gradually increase the time spent, the closeness and the eye contact. Encourage her interaction and imitation. Gradually increase the amount of choice she can have in starting and stopping, or changing to another game.

■ Physically shape her actions. For example, hold her hands to make a clap in 'pat a cake'. Gradually reduce your involvement by loosening your hold and allowing her to take over the movement when she is ready.

■ Starting with your hands over hers, introduce actions, such as push/pull, squeeze, splash, roll, poke, twist, turn, tap, using appropriate toys.

- Play with sand, pouring it over her hands and getting her to pour it over your hands. Play similar games with water in the bath.

- Play floor games with songs and music. Start with her sitting with her back to you, between your legs. Sway and rock, or get her to clap hands to music or familiar rhymes. Turn her briefly towards you within the circle of your arms and then away again. Gradually increase the face to face time during play.

- Hold a musical instrument or a noisy, moving or flashing toy close to your face. Stop the action and move into the child's line of sight saying, 'Do it again?'. Start the toy again and repeat, waiting for her to give you some sign when it stops.

- Develop 'rough and tumble' play and chasing games. Look out for and encourage eye contact, turn taking and anticipation. Introduce lengthy pauses in order to build in anticipation. Wait for her to let you know, in any way she can, that she wants to continue. Play 'chase and tickle', then wait for eye contact before doing it again. Carry her 'piggy back' trying to get her to let you know when she wants you to stop and start. Be careful not to go over the top to the point where she becomes too excited.

See **Unit 3 – Developing obsessions into social play – p41.**

Taking turns

"I can't get Barbara to play games like see-saw with me. I've noticed she never copies me."

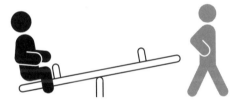

What to look out for

- Children with autism may not imitate movements, actions, expressions or sounds; they may not babble back when their parents talk to them.

- They often do not copy their parents when they wave 'bye bye' or put up their arms to be lifted.

- It can be difficult to teach a child with autism how to take part in turn-taking games, where a sense of 'give and take' is needed.

Things to try

- Blow on Barbara's face or hair or arms. Guide her in exploring **your** face, making sounds or mouth movements in response to her touch. Aim at getting her to 'activate' you, making you stop and start.

- Build anticipation into jumping and stamping games such as '1-2-3-go' and 'Ring o roses'. Make sure you emphasise the build-up to the 'event' (the 'go' or the 'all fall down'), and pause before it happens.

- Encourage her to control the pace in games like 'Row your boat' or 'See-saw'.

- Give her opportunities to choose, eg which game, toy or musical instrument? Limit the choice at first to one of two. Gradually increase the number of things to choose from, but only when she is ready. Allow her to choose, at first by reaching and then by touching or pointing. Take her hands and gently mould these movements, with your hand over hers.

■ Offer choices at mealtimes or when dressing, in a similar way.

■ If you wear dangly earrings, draw her attention to them. Say, 'Look', tap the earrings and make them sway. Then pause briefly, before continuing. Now and again duck into her line of sight to make eye contact if you can, before moving back and tapping the earrings again. Then stop. Don't move. Leave plenty of time because she may look at you. If she does, say, 'Do it again?' and do so.

■ Develop 'two-way interaction' games, such as see-saw or rolling a ball back and forth between you. Push her on a swing (from the front if possible). Show things and offer them to her. Take turns in 'give and take' games. The kind of games or activities which need at least two people are particularly useful when you are trying to encourage her to relate to other children. Things like moving a table together, pushing one another in a cart, holding something for you, or helping with a variety of household chores can all be helpful.

UNIT 2: Communication

Introduction

Generally babies come into the world eager to communicate. They are 'pre-programmed', ready to soak up what they see and hear and to make sense of it. They have an interest in people and faces, and quickly learn to take part, taking turns with us, as if in conversation, even before they have any real speech sounds or words.

Children with autism may not be as eager to communicate. They may not be ready to learn the things which other babies learn naturally and therefore do not have the chance to 'tune in' to language in the same way. They find it very hard to make sense of the things which happen around them. Words may mean very little to them and they may be unable to link what they see with the things being said to them.

Language development occurs through young babies making connections between the sounds they hear, and what happens in the world around them. They learn to predict that someone opening the door will mean they will be lifted out of their cot. At first the language which goes along with these routines makes sense only as part of the routine. Later, when children learn that objects and actions have labels, which do not change from one situation to another, this language makes sense, even outside the routines in which it was first used. Once children know that objects and actions have labels, they begin to learn words for things which capture their interest. They follow an adult's pointing and naming of things, and they learn to point things out themselves, to ask for the word they need.

Young children with autism not only have difficulty making sense of words but also in 'reading' non-verbal messages in facial expressions and gestures. For all of us, these non-verbal clues are very important in helping us to make sense of the whole message. For children with a specific problem in learning words, it is very important for us to help them in any way we can to understand what we mean. We should not forget that children with autism often make sense of things they see more easily than things they hear. This is a strength that we can use. Pictures, symbols, photographs and signs may be helpful.

It is tempting for adults to see the development of speech sounds as being the main building block for developing spoken language. Children **do** move from babbling to words, and babbling is an important part of language development, because it allows babies to practise the movements and sounds which will be needed later. For children with autism, learning to enjoy making speech sounds may eventually encourage them to use sounds with meaning, but children cannot build words and learn about **how** to communicate **just** by being taught how to say sounds. The most important part of language development is **learning to use shared messages**. This means learning to understand and use a **system** of communication with other people, a verbal system and a non-verbal system.

Children without communication problems pick up the rules of conversation very easily, before and alongside the process of learning words. Children with autism do not catch on to the rules of the 'talking game' at all easily. Even those who have some good language skills may still not be able to hold conversations easily, or to use language in the many, many ways that other children do.

Before you start

- For young children with autism, one aim is to help them to enjoy exploring their own lips, tongue, teeth etc and the sounds which they can make. It is important to make any play with sounds **fun**.

- Don't forget, all routines, such as dinner time, bath time, bed time, give children the chance to make sense of the language they hear around them. These are good times to talk about what is happening, even if at first they show little response.

- We want to encourage children to join in with turn-taking play using sounds. This is really a way of practising **conversations** as well as practising making speech sounds.

- Some children with autism may copy words they hear, and name things around them. What is missing is the shared enjoyment in what words mean.

- Remember that we want to **encourage** words. Don't worry if they don't sound quite right to start with.

- When children with autism are struggling to learn to talk, **any** kind of speaking should be seen as an encouraging sign.

- We want to encourage children to learn lots of new words, but we want them to use these words **to talk to people**.

- Many children with autism just 'collect' words, but we need to strike a balance between encouraging new words and encouraging more appropriate use of words.

- Children need a reason to talk. They need to have things to talk about. They need to know the words they want to use. Copying what other people say is one way of learning to talk. Many children go through a phase of echoing.

- We need to be sure that a child has other ways of communicating and learning about talking, **before** we try to reduce the amount of echoing he does.

- For any child with autism, learning to communicate about things which are important to **him** is the best place to begin. That is why we usually begin by teaching children how to ask for what they want.

- Remember that many children with autism continue to do or say things in exactly the same way as they did on the first occasion.

- Be careful how you try to get your message across in the early stages. Children with autism often get set in their ways and teaching a new way to say something at a later time may cause them to become upset or frustrated.

- Learning how to understand messages is one of the most important things in a child's development.

- Remember it is easy to read more into a child's voice, face or movements than was really intended. Adults may think a child is bored or rude, when this is not the case.

- It may take a lot of time and repetition to teach a young child with autism to understand and use spoken language. All of the activities in the Units on social interaction and imagination should be accompanied by spoken language where possible. It is important not to say too much, however. You may feel you need to try some of the activities silently to keep your child's attention, or to add emphasis to your gestures or facial expressions. It is especially important to use expectant pauses to encourage your child to **begin** an interaction.

26

Making sounds

"Sarah doesn't even babble now, although she used to. She sometimes makes noises but they don't sound like speaking."

What to look out for

■ When they are younger, children with autism may babble. Later on the babbling may disappear completely, or may not develop into speech-like sounds.

■ Some children may make sounds which do not appear in English; things like clicking noises, or sucking-in-air noises.

■ Some may babble in long strings. They seem to chatter to themselves at times, but not as if 'talking' to someone else, and rarely to imitate someone.

Things to try

■ To encourage air to come from the lungs through the mouth, play blowing games with bubbles, balloons or pieces of tissue. Use musical instruments, windmills etc. If Sarah is not ready to copy you, see if she will watch you. See if she ever tries out things you have been doing when you are not looking.

■ Encourage lip movements. If she is happy looking in a mirror, or sitting on your knee facing you, encourage her to explore your lips and face by touching and looking. Pull different faces. Change the shape of your lips. Put your tongue in and out, and watch her to see if she will copy you.

■ To encourage Sarah to use the tip of her tongue, try licking activities with lollies, or use sticky paper to make patterns.

■ To encourage her to use her voice, use sound-activated toys such as the Talking Parrot, the Worm in the Apple, the Echo Mic etc. (available from any good toy shop). Use a kazoo. Sing to her frequently, sometimes leaving gaps for her to join in if she will. Make a tape of her sounds or make a tape of **your** babbling to encourage her to copy.

■ Don't forget you may need to use a higher or lower pitch, and a louder, or quieter or longer sound to interest Sarah in what you are doing.

■ Encourage her to imitate and take part in 'conversations'. Begin by copying any sounds she makes as closely as possible. Do this even if she is banging a drum, or tapping a table for example. Pause to allow her to have another turn. Try to build up turn-taking. Sometimes try a new sound, for example a clap, or a different rhythm to a drum beat, to see if she will copy **you.**

■ If Sarah is babbling, copy her speech sounds and sometimes try a different sound to see if **she** will copy **you.** Smile and pause if she looks at you. Try sounds which are very different from the ones she has used, or try sounds that are **nearly** the same. For example 'b' and 'p' sound similar, but 'p' and 's' sound very different. Change the volume or the pitch of the sound. Always be prepared to go back to copying her if she stops copying you.

■ If Sarah is interested in words and letters, use these to encourage sound making. Try saying the sounds, rather than the letter names, as you write them.

Sharing meaning

"I hold things up for Yatin to look at so that he knows what I'm talking about, but I don't think he connects the 'thing' with what I'm saying."

What to look out for

- Some children with autism may use an object for a repetitive activity like tapping. However, they may give no sign of knowing what the object **is**, or what it can be **used for**.

- Other children just repeat words they have heard without seeming to attach them to a particular object or picture. They appear to be practising speaking, but they are not communicating with anyone else.

- Some children with autism may take no notice when an adult tries to draw their attention to an object.

- They may not **show** things to people around them, or look towards them to gain their interest.

Things to try

See **Unit 1 – Play with me – p22**.

- Copy Yatin's actions to help him understand that you are interested in what he is doing. This will encourage **him** to do things to show **you**.

- Encourage him to watch you 'showing off' with silly hats or funny clothes. You could try using face paints and then making different faces to him.

- Use photographs, or a mirror or masks, to encourage Yatin to look at you, himself or other people.

- Show **him** things **you** have done. Point out how things work.

- Use 'hiding and finding' games to build up Yatin's interest in things you are talking about. Try putting things down a long tube and waiting for them to appear. Talk about the object as it disappears and as it re-appears.

- When he has learned to understand a pointing gesture, point to the things you are talking about and say, 'Yatin, look ...'.

- When you talk to Yatin, make sure he knows what it is you are speaking about. Draw his attention to it, by sticking a word or a picture **on** the object.

- Use the same word or phrase each time you talk about a particular object, action or event. Don't be tempted to say too much. Keep what you say simple, and use pauses to encourage Yatin to look at you and the thing you are talking about.

- Teach him how to show things to people. If he understands simple instructions say, '**Show** it to grandad'. If he needs help, walk with him, guiding his hand to show things to people.

Moving on from being used as if you were a 'tool'

"Whenever Joel wants something he takes my arm and drags me to it."

What to look out for

■ Some children with autism seem to use people, as if they were objects, just to get what they want.

■ Some children will throw an adult's arm towards an object to indicate that they want it.

■ Some go through complicated manoeuvres to put someone in the right place or position.

Things to try

See **Unit 1 – Shared attention – p19.**

■ When Joel drags you to something, assume that he is trying to tell you that he wants something and is not just using you.

■ Before you give him what he wants, try to get him to look at you or give any response that shows he is aware of you.

■ Choose, and use, set phrases for different situations, for example, 'Joel wants biscuit', 'Do it again', 'Joel wants to jump'.

■ Leave a pause in the hope that he might copy your phrase, but don't worry if he doesn't. Just say it again for him. **Don't** say, 'Say ___'.

■ Leave objects out in expected places, so that Joel can go and fetch them to show you what he wants. You can encourage him to do this by picking up the object, putting it in his hand, and then taking it from him.

■ If he drags you to the kitchen and you know he wants a drink, encourage him to hold on to his favourite cup and, using your hand to guide his, help him to give it to you. Say a phrase you would like him to use in this situation, for example, 'Want juice', or 'Joel wants ___', with an extended pause in order to encourage him to complete the phrase.

■ You could prompt him in additional ways, for example, by sticking labels/photographs of things he particularly likes on shelves or on the outside of cupboards where they are kept. When he takes you to that place, encourage him to touch the picture.

■ Once Joel regularly shows you what he wants by touching the photo or picture on the cupboard, give him a choice of things by showing him two photos or two pictures. Try not to say anything. Hold up the pictures or show them to him, so that he looks first at one and then at the other. Encourage him to give you, or touch, the one that he wants. Then say, 'Joel wants ___' and give it to him. You may need to guess which one he wants. You know his preferences, and may notice the one he looks at for longer. In any case make sure that he either touches or gives you the picture.

- When you know he can make a choice from pictures or photographs, blu tack them onto a board he can reach, so that he can fetch one to show you what he wants. You will need to teach him what to do by walking him to the board and helping him to take a picture. He may need help a few times. Take away any pictures of the things you **don't** want him to have at any one time.

Understanding gestures

"Even if I make a big show to point something out to Jaswinder, she just stares blankly at my face. She doesn't look where I'm pointing."

What to look out for

- Some children with autism seem totally baffled by the everyday gestures that very young children usually understand. For example, they may not come to a parent if beckoned, or come to outstretched arms.

- Some learn to copy other people's movements, but it is as if they just mirror everything without understanding.

- Some learn to make sense of obvious gestures, like waving bye-bye or pointing, but usually **only** because they have been specially taught how to do so.

- Some do not look for gestures to help them understand their world. For example, they would not go to sit on a chair that someone was patting.

Things to try

- Make the same gesture, over-emphasised, in the same situation, again and again. For example, make sure you have Jaswinder's attention, and then pat her chair before she sits down at mealtimes as you say, 'Jaswinder, sit down'.

- When she seems to follow this gesture at mealtimes, begin to use it at other times and in other places, when you want her to sit down.

- Introduce another gesture in a familiar routine. For example, beckon when you say, 'Come here'. Gradually use this gesture at other times and in other places. You may need to teach each new gesture, one at a time, in this way.

- Use your hands to emphasise the things you are saying, for example, big, little, round, etc.

- Help Jaswinder to follow a point, by pointing to things she is already looking at while you talk about them.

- Point to an object near to her gaze, and try to make sure she looks at it. Tap it, and move it into her line of vision if necessary.

- Use construction toys or puzzles that she enjoys. Point to where the next piece should go, or the piece that she needs next. Use phrases like, 'in here', 'on here', 'this one' as you point.

Learning to use and understand pointing

"Gary climbs up and just gets what he wants. He never points."

What to look out for

- Pointing is something which most young children develop naturally. Children with autism are often late to use this gesture.

- Some children with autism learn to point, but do not understand that someone needs to see them doing so.

- Many children are very slow to use pointing as a way of showing and sharing. They may point to something they want, but not to draw your attention to something which interests them.

- They do not always understand what we mean when **we** point to something.

Things to try

See **Moving on from being used as if you were a 'tool' – p29.**

- When teaching Gary to point, start by using things that interest him.

- Do lots of activities with him where he needs to separate his first finger, eg telephone dialling, pressing switches and buttons, poking holes in dough, drawing in sand and finger painting.

- When he reaches for something, take his outstretched hand and 'mould' his finger into a point so that he touches it.

- Teach him how to choose by offering him a choice of, for example, two foods, two drinks, two pieces of a puzzle. When he reaches for the one he wants, put down the other one. As above, 'mould' his finger into a point so that it touches the chosen object. Do this as often as possible in lots of different situations. Try not to say, 'Point' or, 'Which one do you want ?', but do give him the name of the one he has chosen.

- Put his favourite toy in a place that is difficult to reach. When he reaches for it mould his finger to make a point in the direction of the object.

- At the same time as teaching a 'touch' point, or a 'distance' point (see above) do anything you can to get Gary to look back towards you as well as pointing. For example, you could use a very long pause before you give him the thing he wants. Tap him gently to get him to turn around. Say his name, or put yourself in the line of his vision. Look at him, look back at the object, and look at him again as you give him the object.

- Once Gary can point **and** look at you, expecting you to get what he wants, use more spoken language for him to copy. If he is learning words, say the name of the object concerned, and leave a pause. If you think he doesn't know the word, use a phrase like 'this one'.

- In any game you play with Gary, try to take turns so that he sees **you** pointing and learns to understand what you mean.

■ Having taught Gary how to use pointing in order to choose, you need to demonstrate other types of pointing, especially, 'Look ____'. Point things out to him, in an exaggerated way, whenever you can. Begin by touching the thing you want him to look at, for example in a book. Then start to use 'distance' points, perhaps to an aeroplane in the sky, or to a train going by.

Understanding expressions

"I tried to show Richard I was interested in what he was doing by the look on my face, but he didn't seem to understand."

What to look out for

■ Some children with autism seem not to notice, or cannot 'read' what people mean by the looks on their faces, even when these are exaggerated.

■ Some are baffled when people tease them in fun, for example, 'I'm coming to get you'. The words sound fierce and the child may not notice the smiling face.

■ Some may appear rude in the way they talk, or in the faces they make. They may simply turn their back on people.

Things to try

■ Exaggerate **all** your gestures and expressions. Don't be afraid to look **very** surprised or shocked, or pleased or upset, depending on how you are feeling.

■ Avoid teasing games to begin with, but play anticipation games such as, 'I'm coming to tickle you', with a friendly voice and a smiley face.

■ Keep the message in your face, your voice and your words the **same** to begin with. For example, if you are cross, **look** cross, **sound** cross and **say** cross words. If you are happy ....

■ Use the same expression, with the same words, in similar situations.

■ If Richard understands some language say, 'Look at Daddy's face' and tell him what your expression means. See **Unit 1 – Social awareness and interest – p10.**

■ Look at photographs, pictures of faces and the television. Talk about happy, sad, frightened and excited expressions.

■ Look in a mirror together and practise making different faces.

For more suggestions about keeping messages simple and language fun see **Unit 1 – Social interaction – p9.**

Learning words and what they mean

"Ross will copy words and then say them once or twice, but after that he just drops them. He doesn't get excited about words or tell us things like his brother did."

What to look out for

■ Many children with autism are slow to move from babble to recognisable words.

■ Others may use words once or twice, and then 'lose' them.

■ Their words lack variety and are mostly 'names' of things. Some children become hooked on repeating names over and over.

■ When they are learning words, all children seem to go through a stage where they use a new word either too widely, or too narrowly. For example, 'cat' might mean the family cat, but no other cat. 'Daddy' might be used for any man. Children with autism often carry on doing this much longer than usual.

■ Often children learn a phrase as a whole chunk, but children with autism may never be able to split it into separate words, so that they can use these words in new phrases.

■ Some children learn to repeat complicated sequences. They may count off by heart or recite the alphabet, but with no understanding of what they are saying.

Things to try

■ Use Ross' interests as a way of getting him started with learning new words.

■ Don't get locked into just using labels. For example, with Thomas the Tank Engine we can talk about actions – 'stop', 'go, 'smile', 'laugh', 'speak' – as well as colours, numbers and other descriptions like 'big' and 'small'.

■ Encourage Ross to say words, copying you at first, to ask for things he really wants. You can also help him to say 'more' and 'again' which he could use in lots of situations, for example when he would like **more** juice, **more** yoghurt or would like to have a song or game **again.** This gives you the chance to say lots of different short phrases for Ross to try to copy.

■ Teach him to say 'No' for things he does not want. For example, as he pushes a toy away say, 'No', for him to copy. You will be helping him to make choices. Make sure you accept his 'No' whenever you can.

■ If Ross says something, make sure you respond in some way. Treat it as if he is trying to tell you something. Remember we want him to talk to **people**.

■ Be pleased and respond to any words Ross tries to say, even if they don't sound quite right. Say the word again. For example, if he says 'Tat', you could say 'Yes, cat', but don't insist he practises it until he gets it right.

■ Show Ross how to ask other children for things, either at home or when out visiting. At playgroup, milk time is a good time to do this.

- Make sure there are times when he has to ask for something and cannot just get it himself.

- Avoid coaching Ross so that he recites long lists of things which he does not understand as a party piece.

Using words as more than labels

"Daniel uses lots of words. He can name everything around him, but he still doesn't talk to anyone."

What to look out for

- Some children with autism learn the names of things and use them over and over. They may learn names very readily but ignore other words altogether. It is as if they are collecting labels.

- Often these words are used without being said to anyone in particular. The words are not used to point objects out to other people, or to ask for things.

- The child may start talking when he is alone in the middle of the room, because he doesn't understand what talking is for.

Things to try

- Whenever Daniel names something, respond **as if** he were talking to you. Pick up the object, hold it between you so that he can see both the object and your face, and say, for example, 'Yes, it's a red car'.

- If he names something out of reach or out of sight, respond **as if** he has asked you for it, and give it to him. Persist with this, even if he seems puzzled or a little agitated at first.

- Play giving **and** taking games, where you ask for one object to put away or play with. Then it is Daniel's turn to ask for another one.

- Set up situations where Daniel needs to use one of his 'labels' to ask for something. If he has a favourite car or spinning toy, put this just out of reach where he can see it.

- Talk to Daniel about what you are doing as you are doing it. Play 'hop, skip and jump' type games outside, to give you a chance to talk about actions.

- Touch an object as you talk about it, if you can.

- Talk about properties of objects, such as their colour. Collect lots of different things of the same colour and say the colour name as you touch each one, 'yellow, yellow ...' etc.

- Encourage Daniel to learn words and phrases which are not just labels. Use favourite toys or objects, which he can already name. Introduce action words. For example, say, 'jump', 'go', 'sleep', 'stop', making the toy do the action as you speak. Pause to see if he will ask you to do the action again.

- Stick to a few action words to begin with and use these in lots of different activities. If Daniel enjoys physical games and rough and tumble, you could teach words which he has to use in order to make you do something, for example, 'again' 'tickle' 'jump'.

Understanding language

"Alison only seems to hear part of what we say."

What to look out for

- Some children with autism do not seem interested, or do not respond, when people talk to them. They don't look when called or turn when someone says, 'Where's mummy ?'. They don't respond to things like, 'It's dinner time', or 'Let's go and play outside'.

- Unfortunately, this means that they may appear stubborn or unwilling to do as they are told. It can be hard for parents when relatives or friends, who do not understand, say how naughty their child is.

- A child may start to do something he has been asked to do, but seem to forget half-way through.

- Children may pick up part of something that has been said, but miss the important bit. When told, 'Put your cup on the table', they may just react to the word 'cup' and bring it to you.

- Children may misunderstand what people really mean, and take things too literally. For example, they may hold out a hand if asked, 'Come and give me a hand'.

- Some repeat what others say, in part or completely, often just parroting the last few words. For example, they might say, 'You cold' when asked, 'Are you cold?'. See **Moving on from echoing – p36.**

- Many children with autism ask the same questions over and over again.

Things to try

- Look out for situations when Alison **does** respond to what people say. Then try to use the same words in similar situations. For example, if she turns when you say, 'Daddy's home', stick to this phrase rather than changing it.

- Make a list of phrases the whole family can use, about things which happen often.

- Only use these phrases at times when they really do make sense.

- Use Alison's name to get her attention at the beginning of what you say, not at the end. It may be necessary to gain her attention before speaking, perhaps by tapping her on the arm as you say 'Alison'.

- Use objects to show Alison what is going to happen. For example, show her a spoon and say, dinner time'. Always keep the objects the same, so that she learns to predict what is going to happen. See **Unit 3 – Repetitive activities: Knowing what comes next – p47.**

- When you are playing with her, set things out in a way that makes your intentions very obvious. For example, get out the paper and paints **before** saying, 'We are going to paint'.

- Keep your language simple and demonstrate wherever possible. When a task is more familiar, you can increase her understanding by using slightly different language.

- When Alison is with other children, for example at playgroup, ask staff or helpers to go over any instructions individually with her. Make sure they understand about keeping their language simple, with key words emphasised.

- Always give her **time** to answer a question, to do as you ask or to think of something to say.

- Remember, say things in the order you want them to be done. It might help to prepare a list beforehand so that you don't miss something out. Perhaps you could link what you say to objects or pictures in the right order. See **Unit 3 – Repetitive activities: Knowing what comes next – p47**.

Moving on from echoing

"Whatever I say to Aaron he just repeats it. It's like he can't help himself. I say, 'What are you doing?', and he just says 'You doing?', with my accent."

What to look out for

- Some children with autism seem to learn to talk by copying exactly what they hear other people saying. This is often called **echolalia**.

- Echolalia can be **immediate**, that is, repeated straight after the person has said it, or **delayed**, so that the child learns the phrase and uses it as a chunk at a later time.

- A child may repeat the whole phrase, or only part of what he has heard.

- Other children learn how to make up their own short sentences, but repeat echoed phrases when they don't understand or if they are upset or worried.

- Some children learn whole conversations they have overheard or scripts from TV shows. They can repeat them perfectly right down to tone of voice and posture.

- When given a choice, for example, 'Do you want milk or juice?' some children will echo, 'milk or juice' or will always repeat the last word, 'juice'.

Things to try

- Try to make sure that Adam understands you. Use simple language, and make it as meaningful as possible, for example by using gestures or showing him what you are talking about. Use photographs, symbols or signs to help him understand what will happen next.

- Look for any signs of upset or anxiety. Adam could be echoing to comfort himself.

- Talk to him about things **as they happen**. Try to make comments to him, rather than asking him lots of questions. The use of too many questions can sometimes make echolalia worse.

- Make use of his echoing style, by **giving it meaning**. If he echoes a question like, 'Do you want to go outside?' by repeating 'Go outside', interpret this as if he is asking to go outside, and get ready to go.

- Make the most of Aaron's echoing by using it to teach useful phrases.

- Teach Aaron words he can use in order to get your attention, ask you for help, or ask for something he wants to do etc. The aim is to give him other words to use and thereby reduce his need to echo.

- When greeting Aaron, say 'Hello' rather than 'Hello, Aaron' so that when he echoes you, it sounds appropriate.

Putting words together and learning how to use them

"Adam has learned to name things, but he doesn't put words together yet."

What to look out for

- Some children with autism get stuck at the stage of using only single words.

- Some children stop using old words when they learn new words. That means that the number of words they use doesn't get bigger. Their vocabulary just changes.

- Some talk about the same things, using the same word or phrase in the same way, every day.

Things to try

- Choose times when Adam is really interested, or really wants something, to introduce new words and phrases which can be used in lots of different situations.

- Use simple phrases like, 'Thomas on' (asking for a video), 'help me', 'want it', 'this one' or 'want biscuit', in the hope that he will copy you.

- When he wants something, try to use the word 'want' with words he already knows, as often as you can. For example, 'want it', 'want book', 'want juice'.

- When he wants **help**, see if you can teach him to use a phrase like, 'help me'.

- When he **doesn't want** something, teach him, 'don't like', 'don't want'. It is important that he learns the power of language, so you do need to respect 'don't want' where you can.

- When things **disappear** you can say something like, for example, 'Juice all-gone', or, 'Daddy gone'.

- When he wants something **again**, or more of something say, 'Do it again', or 'More puzzles'.

- You need to give him a good model to copy whenever you can, so if you think he is listening, or when you are taking turns in games with him, use a phrase you would like him to copy. For example, 'Mummy's turn', 'Let's go', 'It's gone', 'No, thank you' etc.

- Don't be afraid to wait for a longer sentence, if you feel Adam may be able to say something more. If he gets **very** cross with you, say the phrase yourself and do whatever it is he wants to do, or stop doing the thing which is annoying him. Each time you come across a similar situation, try again.

Learning about what people mean

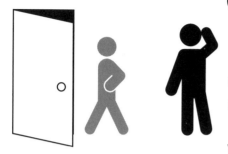

"I said, 'Robin get a plate from the kitchen'. He went in the right direction, but he didn't come back until I shouted, 'Bring the plate back, Robin!'."

What to look out for

- Some children with autism may struggle to make sense of what people are saying. They may not be able to 'read' the real message **behind** the words said to them.

- Some children become confused by people talking to them. They may not be able to work out what is important from the words and gestures used, the tone of the voice and the expressions on people's faces.

- Some children with autism learn to look out for expressions on faces and changes in the way things are said to them. They may then begin to understand that these things are sometimes more important than the spoken words actually used, but this takes time and it will not be easy for them.

- Sometimes, even children who understand about how messages are shared between people, become puzzled by the sayings we often use. Things like 'Pull your socks up', 'Get a move on', 'Cut it out', which have a hidden meaning, may be very confusing for them, because they may take what is said literally.

- Even when children have not fully understood the meaning, they may repeat words and whole phrases which they have heard. Their spoken language may **sound** better than we know their **understanding** of spoken language to be.

Things to try

- Try to avoid using phrases which are likely to really confuse or upset Robin like, 'Give me a hand' or, 'Don't hang about'.

- Encourage him to say when he hasn't understood.

- Try to tell him exactly what you want him to do. Say, 'Bring the book' rather than 'Can you fetch the book?'.

- Use gesture and demonstration to support your spoken language, so that he understands what you are asking or saying. **Show** him and **tell** him at the same time.

- If he doesn't do what you ask, remember it may be because he hasn't understood, **not** because he is being naughty.

- If Robin is interested and can understand, talk about some of the sayings that you use regularly, and explain what they actually mean.

- Draw some pictures, for example of phrases like, 'We've run out of milk', 'He ran into Granny', one with a literal meaning and one with the usual interpretation. Try to make them funny. Match the pictures to the sentences.

Rules of the talking game

"Rosie chatters a lot, but what she says never has anything to do with what other people say. She keeps interrupting and sometimes doesn't even look at who she's talking to."

What to look out for

- Some children with autism do not look at people when they talk, or when they are being spoken to.

- Others stare fixedly at people when they are talking.

- They may not understand about taking turns when they are playing or talking.

- Because they are more interested in what **they** have to say, they may say things in conversation which are totally unconnected with what has just been said by someone else.

Things to try

See **Unit 1 – Looking – p15.**

- Encourage eye contact at the beginning of something you say, by calling Rosie's name and, if necessary, putting your face in her line of gaze.

- If she is not looking say, 'Look' to remind her to look at you when you are talking, or when she is talking.

- Use a 'talking spoon' (or other object) to help her to take turns and stop interrupting. Only the person holding the spoon is allowed to talk. When that person has finished, the spoon is passed to someone else. If Rosie goes to playgroup, staff could use the 'talking spoon' with a small group of children.

- If she changes the subject instead of sticking to the topic of conversation, bring her back by saying, 'I was talking about these flowers, not trains. What sort of flowers do you think they are?'

- If she is talking quite a lot, don't be afraid to try to stop her talking about the same thing over and over again. Try to limit the time, or the place, when she is allowed to talk about her favourite topic. See **Unit 3 – Repetitive activities – p46.**

- Make sure there are times during the day when Rosie has the chance to talk to people.

- Encourage other children and adults to start conversations with her so that she hears how they do it.

- Tell Rosie to look at who she is talking to.

- Remember to allow times when she chooses the topic and you follow her conversational lead.

- In order to help her to take turns, say things like, 'Can Grandma have a turn?', 'Look at Dad's picture', 'Mummy likes that ....'

UNIT 3 : Imagination and the need for sameness

Introduction

Being able to pretend and imagine allows us to think creatively and flexibly. We are not just tied to the way things are. We can plan, anticipate and treat things **as if** they were something else. Imagination can help us put ourselves in someone else's shoes. When pretend play begins to appear it is a sign that imagination is beginning to develop. In children with autism this process occurs very slowly, or in unusual ways, or perhaps not at all.

Autism is a condition with a wide range of severity and the learning difficulties which often go with it can vary. Problems of imagination will, therefore, show themselves in many different ways. Some children never seem interested in what a toy **is** or what it **represents.** They only pay attention to physical features or to some small detail. Other children may use toy tea sets or they may run cars in and out of garages, but they don't act out more complex stories and sequences. Occasionally some children **seem** to be acting out stories and taking the part of particular characters. However, the stories may turn out to be taken from a video or a book. Such play is often very repetitive and if other children are involved they have to act out fixed parts.

Repetitive behaviours and routines are also a feature of autism, and they are linked to the impairment of imagination. People with autism have problems in thinking flexibly and in imagining the way things might be. They have difficulty anticipating and planning the future. The world may, therefore, be a very uncertain place, so they may find re-assurance in setting up routines and patterns which they can control. So much of the world, especially people and the language they use, is hard to make sense of. The easiest option may be to block it out with repetitive activities or very narrow interests.

Problems with repetitive behaviour can show up in many different ways, depending on the child's age, the severity of the autism and any other learning difficulties. Repetitive activities can involve physical actions, such as spinning or arm flapping, which can be combined with objects, so that toys are twiddled, flicked or spun. A child may insist on doing things in a very fixed pattern, or demand that everything is kept exactly the same. Sometimes a child may get hooked on a particular interest or activity, always watching the same video or going on about a very limited topic. Often children with autism are very 'rigid' in they way they learn. They learn to do one particular thing in one particular place, but cannot transfer new skills to new situations.

Developing play skills

Before you start

- The way in which children with autism play can be very unusual. Progress can be very slow. Pretend play may not develop, or at least not in the same way as for other children.

- The play of children with autism is often taken over by their need for 'sameness'. Play becomes another sort of repetitive activity, which can block out other people and cut down on all the opportunities for learning that play usually brings.

- An important aim is to encourage more variety in children's play so that new experience and learning is made possible. This also increases the child's enjoyment and satisfaction. We need to remember that play isn't just about learning. It's also about fun.

- Children with autism also need to learn how to play with people. They need to learn that people can be interesting and fun. Again, this opens up a whole range of new experiences and opportunities to learn.

- A longer term, but very difficult, aim is to help the child towards pretend and imaginative play. He needs to be able to think flexibly in order to hold in mind two different things at the same time: what a thing **is** and what it is **standing for**.

Developing obsessions into social play

"William spins everything he gets his hands on and he cuts us out completely."

What to look out for

- It may not be why they started in the first place, but repetitive activities and obsessions of all kinds may be ways of blocking out people. People make demands, or are just puzzling, so the child tries to cut them out.

- Unfortunately, blocking out people cuts the child off from some very important types of learning.

- Repetitive activities and obsessions can range from simple physical activities, such as spinning or flicking objects, through to wanting only to talk about astronomy or Hoovers.

Things to try

- Join William in his play as suggested in **Learning to share with other children – p44.**

- Move from playing alongside him to swapping toys between you. Watch for awareness from him that you are there and are also spinning things.

- You need to move towards **sharing** an object which spins. Once you are sure William is aware of you and your 'spinner', try having one 'spinner' between the two of you. To start with, **his** turn will need to be a lot longer than yours, but slowly build up your turn and reduce his.

- Once he has accepted this, use different spinners for different sessions.

- Develop any games with the spinner that involve the two of you. Some ideas might be found in **Learning to imitate – p43**. You could also spin the spinner to each other – be creative!

- Once William is enjoying playing **with** you, the spinner could be replaced with a ball and new games tried. Then introduce other sorts of toys.

- Some children with autism find it easier if the adult joins **them** in their obsession, rather than feeling under pressure to change what they are doing. It may feel silly or awkward to start with, but try joining in with the obsession. Copy your child, stopping and starting every so often. Look for signs that he is noticing you or is aware that he is being copied. See if you can develop it into a turn-taking activity.

Using obsessions to develop complex play

"Michael is obsessed with running water."

What to look out for

- Children with autism may play with objects in a very limited, repetitive way. They may be interested in one small detail of a toy, perhaps the wheel of a car, while ignoring the actual car itself. They may become absorbed in tapping, flicking or staring at the car, often from an unusual angle.

- Some obsessions and repetitive activities can look more like pretend play. When looked at more closely, however, they may turn out to have been copied directly from a video. The sequences are repeated by the child in exactly the same way, time and time again.

- Obsessions and repetitive activities can become a problem if they cut the child off from other learning opportunities.

Things to try

- Join Michael in his obsession.

- Put water in different containers with colours or bubbles in it, so that Michael starts to pay attention to different features of the water.

- When you think he is ready, encourage him to play with the water. Show him how to pour, fill or funnel the water, or put it through a water wheel. Aim to make **the water play** just as interesting for him as **watching** the running water.

- Move towards sharing the activity so that the two of you do something together. For example, he could hold the funnel and container, while you pour the water through.

- Develop shared play with different materials. The bath is a really good place for this.

- Encourage imitation, turn-taking and anticipation in the water play.

- Use water in pretend play. Pour 'tea' for the teddy bear's picnic. To begin with he may just copy you, but it is a first step on the way to pretend play.

Learning to imitate

"Hugh lets me play alongside him now but it's like I'm invisible."

What to look out for

- Even when a child with autism doesn't actively avoid other people, he may show no awareness of, or interest in them.

- Many parents feel that their child just uses them as a way of getting things, or just looks at them as if they were no different from objects.

- Copying other people is a very important step. It is a helpful skill to have in its own right. It means that your child is starting to 'tune in' to people. It is also an early step towards pretend play.

Things to try

- Find something which you think will be especially attractive or exciting for Hugh. This doesn't have to be a toy. It can be anything in which he has shown a strong interest. Instead of giving it to Hugh, play with it close to him. The aim is to get him watching you to start with. Then you can tempt him into playing with you, or at least alongside you.

- If this doesn't work, or you cannot think of anything to tempt him, try joining him on his 'territory'. Play with some of the same toys or objects that he plays with, and gradually move closer to him. If he is possessive about his toys, you may need to get a set for yourself and keep it in a separate container.

- Once you have got as far as playing alongside Hugh try these steps:

    - Copy what he does, either with the toys or the noises he is making.
    - Watch him closely to see if he is aware that he is being copied. He might just glance towards you. If you do not get a response, persevere.
    - After that try it again, as often as you can, in **different** play situations. Don't be afraid to exaggerate. Use bigger movements, funnier faces, and louder noises. Let yourself go!

- Once Hugh is aware that you are copying him, try to establish a game where he does something so that **you** will copy **him**. He is moving from doing something which you choose to copy, to deliberately **encouraging** you to copy him.

- Once the copying game is established, see if he will allow you to slip in something new or dramatic and encourage him to copy that as well.

- Play lots and lots of games, copying each other.

Learning to share with other children

"Simon lets me play alongside him but he won't allow his little sister anywhere near him."

What to look out for

- Often, a child with autism plays with objects in order to cut other people out. Sometimes the child just does not seem to be aware of the existence of other people.

- He may allow others to play alongside and may even notice them from time to time, but may reject any attempt by another child to play with him.

- When he does involve others in play, it may be very much on his terms. He may want them to take part in a very limited and repetitive way.

- Children with autism often find being with people quite stressful. They may need time to be alone after any session where you have tried to encourage sharing.

Things to try

- If Simon's sister is old enough, and willing, she could be taught to go through the steps outlined in **Developing obsessions into social play – p41.**

- Set up a play situation in a large space where both children can use the equipment, but be apart from each other. A playground might be a good place to start.

- When you find something Simon really likes, see if you can move his sister closer, for example on a roundabout. You could start by sitting the children opposite each other. Then move them side by side for a short time, maybe just for one quick spin to start with.

- Encourage Simon's sister to copy what he is doing without actually playing **with** him. Tell her, 'It's a copying game'.

First steps towards pretend play

"We bought Dharmesh a play kitchen for Christmas, but he doesn't have a clue what to do with it."

What to look out for

- Some children with autism seem to handle toys and other objects purely for the look and feel of them. Whatever they play with is spun, flicked or lined up, and they may have no interest in what the things actually **are**.

- Some **do** show an interest in toys such as tea sets, cars and garages, toy irons etc. They may understand what these toys are meant to be, and how to use them. Usually though, even if they go through a sequence of activities, there is no imaginative story.

■ Pretend play often starts off as a form of copying. Children with autism may learn to play with a toy in a particular way that they've been shown. It may be much harder for them to work out for themselves new ways of playing.

Things to try

■ Take Dharmesh through a number of steps:

  ■ Bake a cake with him in your kitchen.
  ■ **Pretend** to bake a cake with the real equipment in the kitchen.
  ■ Move the play kitchen into your kitchen and pretend to bake a cake using real pans etc, but put it into the pretend oven.
  ■ In your kitchen pretend to bake a cake with play equipment using the play kitchen.
  ■ Move the play kitchen back to its normal play area and pretend to bake a cake.

■ While going through the above steps, use the word 'pretend'. Say, 'Let's pretend to make a cake'.

■ Every child will go through the stages at different rates. Work at Dharmesh's pace.

■ You will probably need to repeat this process for cooking other things, such as egg and chips.

Moving beyond copying and simple pretend play

"Jamie does play imaginatively, but she always does the same things and it's always with the Playmobil people.".

What to look out for

■ Early pretend play is often a form of copying. The toy Hoover is used just like Mum or Dad use the real one. The play people are set out in just the way they are in the picture on the box.

■ Sometimes this copying has a very rigid pattern. Things can only be arranged in one way. The scene has to be acted out just the way it was in the video.

■ When other people are involved, they are often forced to stick to doing things in exactly the same way.

Things to try

■ Join Jamie in her play. See **Unit 1 – Play with me – p22.**

■ Imitate her routine and encourage 'sharing' the routine: she does a bit, you do a bit. When she accepts this, change your turn, by adding a little bit more. For example with the Playmobil people, instead of the girl going on the slide and onto the swing, you move her from the slide to the roundabout and **then** onto the swing.

- Encourage Jamie to imitate you and include the new bit in her play routine. Try not to keep your turns rigid. Change over at different points. Suggest that she adds a bit when it's her turn.

- If this doesn't work, provide a 'cliff hanger', so there is a compulsion for her to add something new. For example, make the girl fall off the roundabout and have an ambulance nearby, in the hope that Jamie might bring it into the scene.

Repetitive activities

Before you start

- Many people with autism seem to have a need for 'sameness'. Repetitive activities, routines and obsessions may be a way of putting some sort of predictability and order into life. They become a way for the person with autism to keep control and contain anxiety.

- Problems with imagination, and difficulties in making sense of people, reduce the range of activities that the person with autism can enjoy. Repetitive activities may be a soothing way of filling time and finding pleasure.

- To a person with autism other people may be much less predictable and much more demanding than 'things'. Other people may be a nuisance or a threat. Children with autism often use their repetitive activities to shut people out because they get in the way of routines and rituals.

- An important aim is to reduce the child's **need** for repetitive activities and routines To keep anxiety levels low, a child with autism must have some sort of order and pattern in his life.

- Repetitive activities and routines **do** need to be reduced, not only because they get in the way of the child's ability to learn, but also because some of them can be very hard to live with. However, it is not realistic or desirable to try and eliminate them altogether. Aim towards reducing the amount of time spent on repetitive activities, or on limiting them to a particular place or time of day.

- It is just as important, in the longer term, to give the child with autism something to put in the place of repetitive activities – something that is more rewarding and more useful.

- Remember, it is important to help by keeping demands at a reasonable level. Avoid too many changes. Keep language simple and give the child some space of his own.

Structuring the environment

"Harpreet doesn't settle to anything. He seems to be wound up and on the go and he's always running off."

What to look out for

- Some children with autism seem to get frightened by having too much space, or too little.

- They may also find it difficult to cope if they have too much choice.

- It can be difficult for some children with autism to understand or remember your instructions.

- It may be hard for them to organise themselves to get on with tasks, especially if these involve a number of steps.

Things to try

- Help Harpreet to organise the space around him, by linking particular activities to particular places.

- Try to organise what you do by providing clues about what is happening. You could use simple drawings or pictures. Coloured mats can also be linked with activities. When the green mat is on the table Harpreet can play; when it's red it's time to eat.

- Sometimes it helps to mark a physical boundary, especially if you want Harpreet to stay in one place. For example, at mealtimes he could be encouraged to keep himself and his chair on a mat. Carpet samples are very useful for this.

- Tape can also be used to mark boundaries on floors. Harpreet can be encouraged not to cross the line. Later on the tape can be removed when he is able to remember the 'invisible' boundary. See **Unit 1 – Hurt and comfort: making things safe – p13**.

Knowing what comes next

When? When? When? . . .

"Michael goes on and on, asking about when are we going to do this, when are we going to do that. It doesn't matter how many times I answer."

What to look out for

- Some children with autism develop routines. These may involve repetitive physical activities or a determination to do things in a set way.

- Some children talk or ask repeatedly about particular topics.

- Some become very anxious about events that aren't part of familiar routines and will ask again and again about what is going to happen. The actual questioning, and the answers, can turn into another ritual.

Things to try

- Begin by building up a sense of the immediate future for Michael. Talk to him about what is going to happen. You could say, 'First..., and then.....'

- Michael's day can be made much more meaningful if you link the main activities to a photo or some sort of symbol. He can be helped to understand what is going to happen next, by being shown an object or picture. For example, use an inflatable armband to show that you are about to go swimming. To establish this link, you need to build up the connection, by showing Michael the object or a picture of it **every** time the activity is about to happen. If Michael goes to playgroup or nursery, staff may be able to make some suggestions about the best things to try.

Alternatively, you may be able to give them ideas. It is important for all adults working with Michael to use similar approaches.

■ Once Michael connects a few symbols or pictures with what is about to happen next, design a simple timetable showing the symbols for the next two activities. Put one symbol below the other, somewhere your child can see them easily, and use blu-tack so that they can be taken down. Take Michael to the timetable. Help him to remove the top picture and say, 'First ... and then ...', drawing his attention to the second picture. Take the first picture with you **to** the activity. It can be helpful to mark the end of the activity by putting away the picture or symbol in a special envelope or box.

■ Gradually the timetable can be extended, so that half days or days are displayed. Once Michael is making some sense of this system, he should be encouraged to look at the timetable at the start of the day, with each change of activity, and whenever he asks a question about what's going to be happening.

Preparing for change

"If we do something unexpected, or we don't follow her routine, Suresh throws a major tantrum."

What to look out for

■ Many children with autism seem to need routines. They may build these up for themselves, doing things in a special way or organising objects in a particular pattern. They may just become 'hooked' on a part of the everyday routine of family life.

■ Changes to routines can cause major problems. It is as if the child is frightened by the uncertainty of not being able to predict what comes next.

■ Unexpected events can cause the same problems. However, some children with autism seem to accept really major changes, such as a new house or a foreign holiday, while not being able to cope with smaller scale changes.

Things to try

■ Go along with Suresh's need for routines. Build a timetable which clearly shows them. For example:

  ■ Choose a particular picture, line drawing or symbol to go with each part of the daily routine.
  ■ Get Suresh into the habit of taking out the picture at the start of the activity and putting it away at the end. Help her to understand the link between a particular picture and what it stands for.
  ■ Once she seems to understand the link between the pictures and the activities, start to arrange the pictures to show the order of the routine for the next half day. You may be able to build up gradually to a whole day.
  ■ Before you start an activity, go and take the picture. Point out what you are going to do and what will be happening next.
  ■ Once Suresh is used to the timetable, you may be able to introduce one or two new activities. Point these out to her well ahead of their happening. The fact that she gets an advance warning of what's going

to happen, and what will happen afterwards, may help her to cope with change.

■ Some changes may be difficult for Suresh to understand in advance, particularly if the change involves a new place or new people. Video recordings or photographs can be used to prepare her.

■ It may be helpful for Suresh to take something that is familiar into the new situation, in the same way that many children use a cuddly blanket or a soft toy.

■ Use very simple, precise language, that will explain what is happening. Tell Suresh what will happen **after** the unexpected event, for example, 'Then Suresh goes home', and maybe show her a picture of home.

Flappers and flickers: coping with mannerisms and stereotyped movements

"Jack flaps his hands madly whenever he gets upset or excited. He runs up and down on his tip toes, flapping his hands."

What to look out for

■ Children with autism may become anxious and use obsessional or stereotyped behaviour to block out uncertainty.

■ Unusual mannerisms and repetitive movements are often the things which strangers notice first about a child with autism.

■ Such 'oddities' are especially common in younger children. They tend to become less marked as time goes by, but they may continue longer in those who have severe difficulties.

■ The child's mannerisms and movements are often a good indicator of his mood and feelings. They may provide him with pleasant and predictable sensations. In fact they may be the only thing he knows how to do, or over which he has some control. It is worth trying to reduce these movements, so that he appears less 'odd'. However, it is often difficult to stop them altogether, and it may not be fair to try.

Things to try

■ Movements which go on and on may be a sign of anxiety, or Jack may just feel a tremendous need to behave in this way. It may be possible to limit the movements to certain times or places. See **Limiting the object, limiting the place – p50.** and **Rationing the time – p51.**

■ In the long term, these behaviours will only stop if and when Jack finds more rewarding uses for his hands. It is always worth trying to teach new and different ways for him to entertain himself.

■ When you are trying to discourage a mannerism give a consistent prompt, using words and touch. Phrase this in terms of what you want Jack to **do** rather than **not do**. Instead of saying 'Stop that', say, 'Hands down', or 'Hands in pockets'.

■ Some children find it useful to be given something to do with their hands, for example, to carry a bag or to hold a book.

New skills for old obsessions

"Jo is the most expert spinner in the whole world, but it seems to be the only thing she can do."

What to look out for

- A child with autism may seek out the same physical sensations over and over again, for example tapping, smelling, scratching or staring from particular angles.

- Sometimes the repetitive activity can involve whole body movements, such as spinning, jumping or running up and down along the same line.

- Objects are sometimes used in repetitive activities or obsessions, with the child trying to spin, twiddle or flick nearly everything he can get hold of.

Things to try

- Look at **Developing obsessions into social play – P41**. This suggests different ways that you might try to bring other people into Jo's social play.

- At times when Jo **isn't** spinning it is important to try and involve her in something more productive. She needs to be shown and taught that she can get more interesting 'pay-offs' from playing with toys or with another person. The aim is to make **not spinning** more interesting and worthwhile than spinning. This needs to be done very carefully and sensitively. You don't want to make too many demands, because that could drive her back to spinning things.

- Sometimes the obsession can be used to encourage more complicated play. For example, a child who used to spin coins, plates and saucers was taught how to work a spinning top. A fascination with running water can be extended to include pouring, filling, emptying etc.

Limiting the object, limiting the place

"Whatever Graham gets his hands on he twiddles in front of his eyes. Then we just can't get through to him."

What to look out for

- Many children with autism seem to become fascinated with repetitive activities that involve the same pattern of movement over and over again. Twiddling fingers close to the eyes, or rocking from back foot to front foot, are common examples.

- These activities sometimes involve objects, which can be spun or flicked. Some children become obsessed with lining things up, or making 'special' arrangements.

- Some children seem to need to fill their hands with particular objects, so that they are unable to use their hands for anything else.

Things to try

- Firstly, you may be able to limit the **object**:

  - Try to encourage Graham to use one particular 'special object' or a small number of objects. It may well be that he already has a strong favourite. If not, help him to choose something that is very 'twiddleable'.
  - If Graham twiddles other objects, try to remove these and direct him back to the 'special objects'.
  - The aim is for Graham to learn that he **only** twiddles the special object. This can then be available for him at certain times of the day, preferably when it is more socially appropriate.

- An alternative approach is to limit the **places** in which Graham is allowed to twiddle. Try to interrupt the twiddling. Guide Graham or suggest that he move to a place you have chosen, preferably somewhere to which you can limit access. If you choose to do this, then you must allow Graham to twiddle when he is in the chosen place. The aim is to link the place and the twiddling in Graham's mind. If you can do this, then the next aim is to limit the amount of time Graham spends in that place.

- Depending on the type of object Graham twiddles, you may be able to wean him off it by gradually making it smaller and smaller. You could, for example, keep trimming small pieces from it.

Rationing the time

"If we let her, Emily would watch the same video, time after time, day in, day out."

What to look out for

- Sometimes children with autism become fascinated with particular things, such as a favourite book, picture or video and they may want to go on and on about the same narrow interest, whether or not anyone else is interested.

- Some children may act out sequences and characters from videos. This may look like imaginative play but it is more likely to be just imitation.

- Children who develop speech may get 'hooked' on particular topics. They want to talk about Thomas the Tank Engine, dinosaurs or computer games all the time. Their interests may be similar to those of other children of their age. The difference is in the obsessive way in which children with autism pursue their interests, and in the strength of their resistance if anything gets in the way.

Things to try

- Use the video as an incentive. When Emily has gone for a while without watching it, let her watch it as a reward. If she realises that she can watch the video **eventually,** she may cope better with the times when she can't. You may also wish to use the video as a reward at other times.

- If Emily understands some language, it may help to say something like, 'First ..... (whatever you want her to do), and then video'. Always use the same phrase. This lets Emily know that she is not being kept away from the video completely.

- To help Emily grasp the idea of, 'First and then', it may be helpful to use a simple timetable. This can be made with pictures, symbols or with objects related to the activities. For more details see, **Knowing what comes next – p47**.

- Try to get Emily to connect watching her videos with particular parts of the day. The aim is to get her to understand that she **will** be allowed to watch, but only for an hour after tea, for example.

- If Emily is interested in, or understands about time, try setting a cardboard clock next to a real clock, with its hands set to show the time when she can begin watching the video. So, when the clocks match, she can turn it on.

Changing the environment

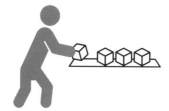

"Living with Craig is like living in a museum. Everything's got to stay in exactly the same place."

What to look out for

- Often, children with autism like things around them to be arranged in certain ways. They may want to impose their own patterns, for example by lining things up obsessively in rows, or they may insist on a particular arrangement of furniture. You may not be aware of this until you try to move the three piece suite around.

- **Gradual** change is often the thing to try for. A very common example is a child who will only poo or wee in a nappy, often only in one particular room, and usually not where we want him to go to the toilet. If there is any predictability to when he does this, try to arrange it so that he is gradually moved closer and closer to the toilet when he uses the nappy. Eventually your aim is to build a link between the activity and the place. You may then need to go through the same gradual process to get your child sitting on the toilet, still in a nappy, and 'performing'.

Things to try

- If possible make sure that Craig has some place that he can organise in the way he wants. His own bedroom is the obvious choice.

- If you are going to have some changes, such as having a new carpet fitted, a very gradual approach will be needed. In an extreme case you might have to go as far as laying the new carpet and then fitting the old one back on top of it. Then, over a period of weeks, bits of the old carpet could be trimmed away until eventually nothing is left of it. (This is an actual example!)

- If Craig reacts badly to even the slightest change, you may need to add an extra step to this approach. Before you make the change, get Craig involved in an activity he really enjoys. While he is involved, make a single tiny change, but put things back to their usual pattern before he finishes the activity. Gradually introduce bigger and bigger changes **during** the activity. Don't move on a step until he seems to have got used to it. Once Craig seems to be coping with change, see if he will tolerate the new pattern once the activity is over.

Changing the way things are done

"Jordan insists we follow exactly the same route to the local shops every time we go. We have to get him ready for bed in exactly the same way every night. It takes forever."

What to look out for

- Some children with autism get hooked on following the same routes and they will object violently if they are made to go a different way.

- Other repetitive activities take the form of rituals which the child invents for himself. Some children **'have'** to touch or tap things along the route.

- Sometimes the routines start off as part of the everyday routine of family life. The trouble is that it then has to be repeated in precisely the same way every single time.

- Elaborate bedtime routines are very common in children with autism.

- Some children insist that everyone sits down at mealtimes in the same order and in the same places.

Things to try

- Try to reduce the length of time it takes for Jordan to get through one of his routines. Start off with one bit or step in the routine. It can be helpful to introduce an artificial signal, such as a kitchen timer, to mark the end of the step. Initially this should be set so that the step takes its usual time. Once Jordan comes to expect the signal as part of the routine, set it for shorter and shorter intervals.

- If the routine seems to have lots of steps and stages, try to miss out the shortest, smallest or apparently least important step. Jordan might find this easier to accept if given a timetable which leaves out the smallest steps. See **Preparing for change – p48**.

- When Jordan becomes comfortable with the timetable, then you may slowly be able to remove more steps from the routine. At this stage it is also worth introducing slight variations to some of the steps, in order to encourage him to be a little more tolerant of change.

Helping with generalisation

"Mohammed will eat cheese at nursery, but he won't touch it at home."

What to look out for

- Problems with imagination and a 'need for sameness' affect the way children with autism learn new skills and put them to use.
- Children may learn to carry out a particular skill in a particular way, for instance how to put on a vest. If something is then changed slightly, for example, if they have to put on a T-shirt, they may find it impossible to cope.

- Children often link particular activities to particular settings. They might draw pictures at school, but insist on only scribbling or colouring at home.

- Sometimes they may need the instructions to be given in exactly the same way, or they will only take notice of one particular person.

Things to try

- Find ways of 'building bridges' between nursery and home. Try to connect eating in the nursery with something that Mohammed associates with it. Then introduce it to the other setting. For instance:

  - Nursery staff could make sure that Mohammed always eats his cheese off a particular plate.
  - The plate and bit of cheese could be packed in his bag (with Mohammed watching).
  - He could be given the same plate and cheese at home. Hopefully the plate will act as a sort of 'trigger' at mealtimes.
  - **Gradually** nursery staff could then get Mohammed used to eating cheese off different plates.

- When Mohammed has learned to do a particular thing in one setting, for one person, increased flexibility should be worked on in a very systematic but gradual way. Vary one bit at a time:

  - Gradually vary the sort of instruction which is given.
  - Vary or reduce the sorts of prompts or encouragement that is given.
  - Change parts of the task or exactly what Mohammed is required to do.
  - Bring another person into the situation and let them slowly take over. The aim is to introduce enough change and variation to stop Mohammed becoming hooked on one pattern.

- It may be difficult to develop flexibility in a situation where Mohammed has just learned something new. He may be fixed on this new activity always happening in the same place. When you wish to transfer the skills to a new situation, try to copy as much as you can of the original situation. For example, try to use the same instructions and the same objects etc.

- You could try showing Mohammed a video of him doing something at Nursery which you want him to do at home, or vice versa.

Useful addresses

THE NATIONAL AUTISTIC SOCIETY
Headquarters
393 City Road, London EC1V 1NE
Switchboard: 0171 833 2299
Fax: 0171 833 9666

Autism Helpline: 0171 903 3555
This is a written and telephone enquiry service with the phone line open
between 10 and 12 weekday mornings – offers advice and support to parents,
carers and people with autism and Asperger syndrome.
Fundraising: 0171 903 3522
Information: 0171 903 3599
This is a written and telephone enquiry service with the phone line open
between 10 am and 4 pm weekdays – offers information and advice on all
aspects of autism, NAS Services and related topics to professionals, students,
researchers, voluntary organisations. In addition there is a library that parents
and researchers can use by appointment only.
Press: 0171 903 3593
Prospects: Supported Employment Scheme: 0171 903 3580
(Prospects is a supported employment service for adults with autism and
Asperger syndrome.)
Publications: 0171 903 3595
(The Publications Department has one of the best lists on autism and Asperger
syndrome in the country – catalogues will be sent out on request.)

Scottish Office
Suite 3, 111 Union Street, Glasgow
Strathclyde G1 3TA
Tel: 0141 221 8090
Fax: 0141 221 8118

Welsh Office
William Knox House, Suite C1,
Britannic Way, Llandarcy, Neath
West Glamorgan SA10 6EL
Tel: 01792 815915
Fax: 01792 815911

Services Division – for details of NAS schools and adult centres
Church House
Church Road
Filton
Bristol
BS12 7BD
Tel: 0117 987 2575
Fax: 0117 987 2576

Development and Outreach and Training
Castle Heights
4th Floor
72 Maid Marian Way
Nottingham
NG1 6BJ
Tel: 0115 911 3360
Fax: 0115 911 2259

Training
Tel: 0115 911 3363
Fax: 0115 911 3362
(Training Services offers various courses for parents and professionals relating to the autistic spectrum. Tailor-made courses are also available to groups.)

Volunteers co-ordination
Tel: 0115 911 3369
Fax: 0115 911 3362
(The Volunteering Network co-ordinates nationwide parent to parent and befriending schemes. The schemes are available to parents of people with autistic spectrum disorders.)

The Centre for Social and Communication Disorders
Elliot House
113 Masons Hill
Bromley
Kent
BR2 9HT
Tel: 0181 466 0098
Fax: 0181 466 0118

Details of the authors

LEICESTERSHIRE AUTISM OUTREACH TEAM
Western Annexe
County Hall
Glenfield
Leicester
LE3 8RF
Tel: 0116 265 6691

EDUCATIONAL PSYCHOLOGY SERVICE
Room 16/17
County Hall
Glenfield
Leicester
LE3 8RF
Tel: 0116 265 6699

SPEECH & LANGUAGE THERAPY SERVICE
Prince Philip House
St Matthews Community Centre
Malabar Road
Leicester
Tel: 0116 224 4670

To find helpline numbers and addresses of support services in your area, please contact your Local Education Department or Health Authority.